JUMP-START
YOUR DAY
WITH *gratitude*

D0377731

This Journal Belongs to:

Jude Voci

✉ Email us at FREEBIES @ JUNELUCY.COM
to get a FREE printable download!

FOR A LITTLE INSPIRATION
Follow along at:

⬚ @JUNEANDLUCY

⬚ @JUNEANDLUCY

WWW. JUNELUCY.COM

Shop our other books at
www.junelucy.com

For questions and customer service, email us at
support@junelucy.com

Practicing Gratitude: the basics

With work, family, appointments, deadlines, and responsibilities, it can feel like there is no time to stop and smell the coffee, not to mention the roses! The art of practicing gratitude involves taking a few short moments each day to reflect on our life and treasure the moments that make the day sparkle. The big ones (Getting married! Graduating! Spending time with a loved one!) may be obvious, but finding gratitude in the small, quiet moments is just as important. Maybe you got to enjoy a warm mug of your favorite chai tea. Maybe you finished that load of laundry that's been taunting you for a week. Or maybe it's as simple as a friendly wave from a neighbor. Taking note of things to be grateful for is linked to a number of positive benefits.

INCREASE POSITIVITY AND OPTIMISM

Documenting the people, places, things, and events that we are grateful for is a sure-fire way to put us on track for happiness and positivity. When we are feeling down, thinking of just a few things to be grateful for (a nap, a warm meal, a call with a friend) can help lift our spirits. And when we feel alright, documenting gratitude can keep us grounded and optimistic.

IMPROVE SLEEP QUALITY AND LOWER STRESS

Taking a few minutes before bed to reflect on what we have to be grateful for is thought to help clear the mind of worry and encourage better sleep. With all the things to worry about in a given day, it is helpful to think of a couple of things that bring joy into our lives. This sets us up for a restful slumber.

IMPROVE SELF-ESTEEM

A popular study showed that athletes who kept a gratitude journal improved their self-esteem leading to better performance. When we document the personal qualities we are grateful for and the positive aspects of our life, we hold ourselves in higher regard and have more appreciation for the lives we are living.

This journal contains space for you to reflect on the day ahead and again at the end of the day. The magical part of gratitude journaling is that it only takes a few minutes a day to reap all of the benefits. So snuggle up with some tea and this notebook and start getting grateful!

DATE: Aug 23 '21   S (M) T W T F S

I AM GRATEFUL FOR:
1. fresh mango and papaya
2. enough sleep
3. my cozy bed

WHAT CAN I DO TO MAKE TODAY GREAT?
I will chat with my doctor
re breathing problems

WHAT WERE THE BEST MOMENTS FROM TODAY?
My doctor was helpful
I prepared Nick's birthday
gift

DATE: _____   S M T W T F S

I AM GRATEFUL FOR:
1. a warm shower
2. my faith in God
3.

WHAT CAN I DO TO MAKE TODAY GREAT?
Take ownership in improving my
health by eating better food.

WHAT WERE THE BEST MOMENTS FROM TODAY?

DATE: Aug 30   S (M) T W T F S

I AM GRATEFUL FOR:

1. time in Tuwanek
2. Nick ~ his love
3. a relaxing day CN

WHAT CAN I DO TO MAKE TODAY GREAT?

be present to Nick
tidy up
Speak with Lip.

WHAT WERE THE BEST MOMENTS FROM TODAY?

DATE: _____   S M T W T F S

I AM GRATEFUL FOR:

1. _____
2. _____
3. _____

WHAT CAN I DO TO MAKE TODAY GREAT?

WHAT WERE THE BEST MOMENTS FROM TODAY?

DATE: _____ S M T W T F S

I AM GRATEFUL FOR:

1. _____

2. _____

3. _____

WHAT CAN I DO TO MAKE TODAY GREAT?

_____

_____

_____

WHAT WERE THE BEST MOMENTS FROM TODAY?

_____

_____

_____

DATE: _____ S M T W T F S

I AM GRATEFUL FOR:

1. _____

2. _____

3. _____

WHAT CAN I DO TO MAKE TODAY GREAT?

_____

_____

_____

WHAT WERE THE BEST MOMENTS FROM TODAY?

_____

_____

_____

The happiness of your life depends on the quality of your thoughts.

DATE: _____ S M T W T F S

I AM GRATEFUL FOR:

1. _____

2. _____

3. _____

WHAT CAN I DO TO MAKE TODAY GREAT?

_____

_____

_____

WHAT WERE THE BEST MOMENTS FROM TODAY?

_____

_____

_____

DATE: _____ S M T W T F S

I AM GRATEFUL FOR:

1. _____

2. _____

3. _____

WHAT CAN I DO TO MAKE TODAY GREAT?

_____

_____

_____

WHAT WERE THE BEST MOMENTS FROM TODAY?

_____

_____

_____

DATE: _____ S M T W T F S

I AM GRATEFUL FOR:

1. _____

2. _____

3. _____

WHAT CAN I DO TO MAKE TODAY GREAT?

_____

_____

_____

WHAT WERE THE BEST MOMENTS FROM TODAY?

_____

_____

DATE: _____ S M T W T F S

I AM GRATEFUL FOR:

1. _____

2. _____

3. _____

WHAT CAN I DO TO MAKE TODAY GREAT?

_____

_____

_____

WHAT WERE THE BEST MOMENTS FROM TODAY?

_____

_____

_____

DATE: _____ S M T W T F S

I AM GRATEFUL FOR:

1. _____

2. _____

3. _____

WHAT CAN I DO TO MAKE TODAY GREAT?

_____

_____

_____

WHAT WERE THE BEST MOMENTS FROM TODAY?

_____

_____

_____

DATE: _____ S M T W T F S

I AM GRATEFUL FOR:

1. _____

2. _____

3. _____

WHAT CAN I DO TO MAKE TODAY GREAT?

_____

_____

_____

WHAT WERE THE BEST MOMENTS FROM TODAY?

_____

_____

_____

Gratitude turns what we have into enough.

DATE: _____ S M T W T F S

I AM GRATEFUL FOR:

1. _____

2. _____

3. _____

WHAT CAN I DO TO MAKE TODAY GREAT?

_____

_____

_____

WHAT WERE THE BEST MOMENTS FROM TODAY?

_____

_____

_____

DATE: _____ S M T W T F S

I AM GRATEFUL FOR:

1. _____

2. _____

3. _____

WHAT CAN I DO TO MAKE TODAY GREAT?

_____

_____

_____

WHAT WERE THE BEST MOMENTS FROM TODAY?

_____

_____

_____

DATE: _____ S M T W T F S

I AM GRATEFUL FOR:

1. _____

2. _____

3. _____

WHAT CAN I DO TO MAKE TODAY GREAT?

_____

_____

_____

WHAT WERE THE BEST MOMENTS FROM TODAY?

_____

_____

_____

DATE: _____ S M T W T F S

I AM GRATEFUL FOR:

1. _____

2. _____

3. _____

WHAT CAN I DO TO MAKE TODAY GREAT?

_____

_____

_____

WHAT WERE THE BEST MOMENTS FROM TODAY?

_____

_____

_____

reflection

Recall a cherished experience.

DATE: _____ S M T W T F S

I AM GRATEFUL FOR:

1. _____

2. _____

3. _____

WHAT CAN I DO TO MAKE TODAY GREAT?

_____

_____

_____

WHAT WERE THE BEST MOMENTS FROM TODAY?

_____

_____

_____

DATE: _____ S M T W T F S

I AM GRATEFUL FOR:

1. _____

2. _____

3. _____

WHAT CAN I DO TO MAKE TODAY GREAT?

_____

_____

_____

WHAT WERE THE BEST MOMENTS FROM TODAY?

_____

_____

_____

DATE: _____ S M T W T F S

I AM GRATEFUL FOR:

1. _____

2. _____

3. _____

WHAT CAN I DO TO MAKE TODAY GREAT?

_____

_____

_____

WHAT WERE THE BEST MOMENTS FROM TODAY?

_____

_____

_____

DATE: _____ S M T W T F S

I AM GRATEFUL FOR:

1. _____

2. _____

3. _____

WHAT CAN I DO TO MAKE TODAY GREAT?

_____

_____

_____

WHAT WERE THE BEST MOMENTS FROM TODAY?

_____

_____

_____

DATE: _____ S M T W T F S

I AM GRATEFUL FOR:

1. _____

2. _____

3. _____

WHAT CAN I DO TO MAKE TODAY GREAT?

_____

_____

_____

WHAT WERE THE BEST MOMENTS FROM TODAY?

_____

_____

_____

DATE: _____ S M T W T F S

I AM GRATEFUL FOR:

1. _____

2. _____

3. _____

WHAT CAN I DO TO MAKE TODAY GREAT?

_____

_____

_____

WHAT WERE THE BEST MOMENTS FROM TODAY?

_____

_____

_____

All good things come from gratitude.

DATE: _____ S M T W T F S

I AM GRATEFUL FOR:

1. _____

2. _____

3. _____

WHAT CAN I DO TO MAKE TODAY GREAT?

_____

_____

_____

WHAT WERE THE BEST MOMENTS FROM TODAY?

_____

_____

_____

DATE: _____ S M T W T F S

I AM GRATEFUL FOR:

1. _____

2. _____

3. _____

WHAT CAN I DO TO MAKE TODAY GREAT?

_____

_____

_____

WHAT WERE THE BEST MOMENTS FROM TODAY?

_____

_____

_____

DATE: _____ S M T W T F S

I AM GRATEFUL FOR:

1. _____

2. _____

3. _____

WHAT CAN I DO TO MAKE TODAY GREAT?

_____

_____

_____

WHAT WERE THE BEST MOMENTS FROM TODAY?

_____

_____

_____

DATE: _____ S M T W T F S

I AM GRATEFUL FOR:

1. _____

2. _____

3. _____

WHAT CAN I DO TO MAKE TODAY GREAT?

_____

_____

_____

WHAT WERE THE BEST MOMENTS FROM TODAY?

_____

_____

_____

DATE: _____ S M T W T F S

I AM GRATEFUL FOR:

1. _____

2. _____

3. _____

WHAT CAN I DO TO MAKE TODAY GREAT?

_____

_____

_____

WHAT WERE THE BEST MOMENTS FROM TODAY?

_____

_____

_____

DATE: _____ S M T W T F S

I AM GRATEFUL FOR:

1. _____

2. _____

3. _____

WHAT CAN I DO TO MAKE TODAY GREAT?

_____

_____

_____

WHAT WERE THE BEST MOMENTS FROM TODAY?

_____

_____

_____

Gratitude teaches you to fall in love with the life you are already living.

DATE: _____ S M T W T F S

I AM GRATEFUL FOR:

1. _____

2. _____

3. _____

WHAT CAN I DO TO MAKE TODAY GREAT?

_____

_____

_____

WHAT WERE THE BEST MOMENTS FROM TODAY?

_____

_____

_____

DATE: _____ S M T W T F S

I AM GRATEFUL FOR:

1. _____

2. _____

3. _____

WHAT CAN I DO TO MAKE TODAY GREAT?

_____

_____

_____

WHAT WERE THE BEST MOMENTS FROM TODAY?

_____

_____

DATE: _____ S M T W T F S

I AM GRATEFUL FOR:

1. _____

2. _____

3. _____

WHAT CAN I DO TO MAKE TODAY GREAT?

_____

_____

_____

WHAT WERE THE BEST MOMENTS FROM TODAY?

_____

_____

_____

DATE: _____ S M T W T F S

I AM GRATEFUL FOR:

1. _____

2. _____

3. _____

WHAT CAN I DO TO MAKE TODAY GREAT?

_____

_____

_____

WHAT WERE THE BEST MOMENTS FROM TODAY?

_____

_____

reflection

How has someone shown
you love recently?

DATE: _____ S M T W T F S

I AM GRATEFUL FOR:

1. _____

2. _____

3. _____

WHAT CAN I DO TO MAKE TODAY GREAT?

_____

_____

_____

WHAT WERE THE BEST MOMENTS FROM TODAY?

_____

_____

_____

DATE: _____ S M T W T F S

I AM GRATEFUL FOR:

1. _____

2. _____

3. _____

WHAT CAN I DO TO MAKE TODAY GREAT?

_____

_____

_____

WHAT WERE THE BEST MOMENTS FROM TODAY?

_____

_____

_____

DATE: _____ S M T W T F S

I AM GRATEFUL FOR:

1. _____
2. _____
3. _____

WHAT CAN I DO TO MAKE TODAY GREAT?

_____

_____

_____

WHAT WERE THE BEST MOMENTS FROM TODAY?

_____

_____

_____

DATE: _____ S M T W T F S

I AM GRATEFUL FOR:

1. _____
2. _____
3. _____

WHAT CAN I DO TO MAKE TODAY GREAT?

_____

_____

_____

WHAT WERE THE BEST MOMENTS FROM TODAY?

_____

_____

_____

DATE: _____ S M T W T F S

I AM GRATEFUL FOR:

1. _____

2. _____

3. _____

WHAT CAN I DO TO MAKE TODAY GREAT?

_____

_____

_____

WHAT WERE THE BEST MOMENTS FROM TODAY?

_____

_____

_____

DATE: _____ S M T W T F S

I AM GRATEFUL FOR:

1. _____

2. _____

3. _____

WHAT CAN I DO TO MAKE TODAY GREAT?

_____

_____

_____

WHAT WERE THE BEST MOMENTS FROM TODAY?

_____

_____

_____

The time to be grateful is always.

DATE: _____ S M T W T F S

I AM GRATEFUL FOR:

1. _____

2. _____

3. _____

WHAT CAN I DO TO MAKE TODAY GREAT?

_____

_____

_____

WHAT WERE THE BEST MOMENTS FROM TODAY?

_____

_____

_____

DATE: _____ S M T W T F S

I AM GRATEFUL FOR:

1. _____

2. _____

3. _____

WHAT CAN I DO TO MAKE TODAY GREAT?

_____

_____

_____

WHAT WERE THE BEST MOMENTS FROM TODAY?

_____

_____

_____

DATE: _____ S M T W T F S

I AM GRATEFUL FOR:

1. _____

2. _____

3. _____

WHAT CAN I DO TO MAKE TODAY GREAT?

_____

_____

_____

WHAT WERE THE BEST MOMENTS FROM TODAY?

_____

_____

DATE: _____ S M T W T F S

I AM GRATEFUL FOR:

1. _____

2. _____

3. _____

WHAT CAN I DO TO MAKE TODAY GREAT?

_____

_____

_____

WHAT WERE THE BEST MOMENTS FROM TODAY?

_____

_____

_____

DATE: _____ S M T W T F S

I AM GRATEFUL FOR:

1. _____

2. _____

3. _____

WHAT CAN I DO TO MAKE TODAY GREAT?

_____

_____

_____

WHAT WERE THE BEST MOMENTS FROM TODAY?

_____

_____

DATE: _____ S M T W T F S

I AM GRATEFUL FOR:

1. _____

2. _____

3. _____

WHAT CAN I DO TO MAKE TODAY GREAT?

_____

_____

_____

WHAT WERE THE BEST MOMENTS FROM TODAY?

_____

_____

_____

Gratitude is the best way out of comparison.

DATE: _____ S M T W T F S

I AM GRATEFUL FOR:

1. _____

2. _____

3. _____

WHAT CAN I DO TO MAKE TODAY GREAT?

_____

_____

_____

WHAT WERE THE BEST MOMENTS FROM TODAY?

_____

_____

_____

DATE: _____ S M T W T F S

I AM GRATEFUL FOR:

1. _____

2. _____

3. _____

WHAT CAN I DO TO MAKE TODAY GREAT?

_____

_____

_____

WHAT WERE THE BEST MOMENTS FROM TODAY?

_____

_____

_____

DATE: _____ S M T W T F S

I AM GRATEFUL FOR:

1. _____

2. _____

3. _____

WHAT CAN I DO TO MAKE TODAY GREAT?

_____

_____

_____

WHAT WERE THE BEST MOMENTS FROM TODAY?

_____

_____

_____

DATE: _____ S M T W T F S

I AM GRATEFUL FOR:

1. _____

2. _____

3. _____

WHAT CAN I DO TO MAKE TODAY GREAT?

_____

_____

_____

WHAT WERE THE BEST MOMENTS FROM TODAY?

_____

_____

_____

reflection

Offer gratitude for your body.
List some ways your body
serves you.

DATE: _____ S M T W T F S

I AM GRATEFUL FOR:

1. _____

2. _____

3. _____

WHAT CAN I DO TO MAKE TODAY GREAT?

_____

_____

_____

WHAT WERE THE BEST MOMENTS FROM TODAY?

_____

_____

_____

DATE: _____ S M T W T F S

I AM GRATEFUL FOR:

1. _____

2. _____

3. _____

WHAT CAN I DO TO MAKE TODAY GREAT?

_____

_____

_____

WHAT WERE THE BEST MOMENTS FROM TODAY?

_____

_____

_____

DATE: _____ S M T W T F S

I AM GRATEFUL FOR:

1. _____

2. _____

3. _____

WHAT CAN I DO TO MAKE TODAY GREAT?

_____

_____

_____

WHAT WERE THE BEST MOMENTS FROM TODAY?

_____

_____

_____

DATE: _____ S M T W T F S

I AM GRATEFUL FOR:

1. _____

2. _____

3. _____

WHAT CAN I DO TO MAKE TODAY GREAT?

_____

_____

_____

WHAT WERE THE BEST MOMENTS FROM TODAY?

_____

_____

_____

DATE: _____ S M T W T F S

I AM GRATEFUL FOR:

1. _____

2. _____

3. _____

WHAT CAN I DO TO MAKE TODAY GREAT?

_____

_____

_____

WHAT WERE THE BEST MOMENTS FROM TODAY?

_____

_____

_____

DATE: _____ S M T W T F S

I AM GRATEFUL FOR:

1. _____

2. _____

3. _____

WHAT CAN I DO TO MAKE TODAY GREAT?

_____

_____

_____

WHAT WERE THE BEST MOMENTS FROM TODAY?

_____

_____

_____

Happy are those who know it's the little things that mean the most.

DATE: _____ S M T W T F S

I AM GRATEFUL FOR:

1. _____
2. _____
3. _____

WHAT CAN I DO TO MAKE TODAY GREAT?

_____

_____

WHAT WERE THE BEST MOMENTS FROM TODAY?

_____

_____

DATE: _____ S M T W T F S

I AM GRATEFUL FOR:

1. _____

2. _____

3. _____

WHAT CAN I DO TO MAKE TODAY GREAT?

_____

_____

_____

WHAT WERE THE BEST MOMENTS FROM TODAY?

_____

_____

_____

DATE: _____ S M T W T F S

I AM GRATEFUL FOR:

1. _____

2. _____

3. _____

WHAT CAN I DO TO MAKE TODAY GREAT?

_____

_____

_____

WHAT WERE THE BEST MOMENTS FROM TODAY?

_____

_____

_____

DATE: _____ S M T W T F S

I AM GRATEFUL FOR:

1. _____

2. _____

3. _____

WHAT CAN I DO TO MAKE TODAY GREAT?

_____

_____

_____

WHAT WERE THE BEST MOMENTS FROM TODAY?

_____

_____

_____

DATE: _____ S M T W T F S

I AM GRATEFUL FOR:

1. _____

2. _____

3. _____

WHAT CAN I DO TO MAKE TODAY GREAT?

_____

_____

_____

WHAT WERE THE BEST MOMENTS FROM TODAY?

_____

_____

_____

DATE: _____ S M T W T F S

I AM GRATEFUL FOR:

1. _____

2. _____

3. _____

WHAT CAN I DO TO MAKE TODAY GREAT?

_____

_____

WHAT WERE THE BEST MOMENTS FROM TODAY?

_____

_____

_____

With enough gratitude, miracles start to appear everywhere.

DATE: _____ S M T W T F S

I AM GRATEFUL FOR:

1. _____

2. _____

3. _____

WHAT CAN I DO TO MAKE TODAY GREAT?

_____

_____

_____

WHAT WERE THE BEST MOMENTS FROM TODAY?

_____

_____

_____

DATE: _____ S M T W T F S

I AM GRATEFUL FOR:

1. _____

2. _____

3. _____

WHAT CAN I DO TO MAKE TODAY GREAT?

_____

_____

_____

WHAT WERE THE BEST MOMENTS FROM TODAY?

_____

_____

DATE: _____ S M T W T F S

I AM GRATEFUL FOR:

1. _____

2. _____

3. _____

WHAT CAN I DO TO MAKE TODAY GREAT?

_____

_____

_____

WHAT WERE THE BEST MOMENTS FROM TODAY?

_____

_____

_____

DATE: _____ S M T W T F S

I AM GRATEFUL FOR:

1. _____

2. _____

3. _____

WHAT CAN I DO TO MAKE TODAY GREAT?

_____

_____

_____

WHAT WERE THE BEST MOMENTS FROM TODAY?

_____

_____

reflection

Note the things you love
about the outdoors.

DATE: _____ S M T W T F S

I AM GRATEFUL FOR:

1. _____

2. _____

3. _____

WHAT CAN I DO TO MAKE TODAY GREAT?

_____

_____

_____

WHAT WERE THE BEST MOMENTS FROM TODAY?

_____

_____

_____

DATE: _____ S M T W T F S

I AM GRATEFUL FOR:

1. _____

2. _____

3. _____

WHAT CAN I DO TO MAKE TODAY GREAT?

_____

_____

_____

WHAT WERE THE BEST MOMENTS FROM TODAY?

_____

_____

_____

DATE: _____ S M T W T F S

I AM GRATEFUL FOR:

1. _____

2. _____

3. _____

WHAT CAN I DO TO MAKE TODAY GREAT?

_____

_____

WHAT WERE THE BEST MOMENTS FROM TODAY?

_____

_____

DATE: _____ S M T W T F S

I AM GRATEFUL FOR:

1. _____

2. _____

3. _____

WHAT CAN I DO TO MAKE TODAY GREAT?

_____

_____

WHAT WERE THE BEST MOMENTS FROM TODAY?

_____

_____

DATE: _____ S M T W T F S

I AM GRATEFUL FOR:

1. _____

2. _____

3. _____

WHAT CAN I DO TO MAKE TODAY GREAT?

_____

_____

_____

WHAT WERE THE BEST MOMENTS FROM TODAY?

_____

_____

_____

DATE: _____ S M T W T F S

I AM GRATEFUL FOR:

1. _____

2. _____

3. _____

WHAT CAN I DO TO MAKE TODAY GREAT?

_____

_____

_____

WHAT WERE THE BEST MOMENTS FROM TODAY?

_____

_____

_____

It is by being grateful that we achieve greatness.

DATE: _____ S M T W T F S

I AM GRATEFUL FOR:

1. _____

2. _____

3. _____

WHAT CAN I DO TO MAKE TODAY GREAT?

_____

_____

_____

WHAT WERE THE BEST MOMENTS FROM TODAY?

_____

_____

_____

DATE: _____ S M T W T F S

I AM GRATEFUL FOR:

1. _____

2. _____

3. _____

WHAT CAN I DO TO MAKE TODAY GREAT?

_____

_____

_____

WHAT WERE THE BEST MOMENTS FROM TODAY?

_____

_____

_____

DATE: _____ S M T W T F S

I AM GRATEFUL FOR:

1. _____

2. _____

3. _____

WHAT CAN I DO TO MAKE TODAY GREAT?

_____

_____

_____

WHAT WERE THE BEST MOMENTS FROM TODAY?

_____

_____

_____

DATE: _____ S M T W T F S

I AM GRATEFUL FOR:

1. _____

2. _____

3. _____

WHAT CAN I DO TO MAKE TODAY GREAT?

_____

_____

_____

WHAT WERE THE BEST MOMENTS FROM TODAY?

_____

_____

_____

DATE: _____ S M T W T F S

I AM GRATEFUL FOR:

1. _____

2. _____

3. _____

WHAT CAN I DO TO MAKE TODAY GREAT?

_____

_____

_____

WHAT WERE THE BEST MOMENTS FROM TODAY?

_____

_____

_____

DATE: _____ S M T W T F S

I AM GRATEFUL FOR:

1. _____

2. _____

3. _____

WHAT CAN I DO TO MAKE TODAY GREAT?

_____

_____

_____

WHAT WERE THE BEST MOMENTS FROM TODAY?

_____

_____

_____

The root of joy is gratitude.

DATE: _____ S M T W T F S

I AM GRATEFUL FOR:

1. _____
2. _____
3. _____

WHAT CAN I DO TO MAKE TODAY GREAT?

_____
_____
_____

WHAT WERE THE BEST MOMENTS FROM TODAY?

_____
_____
_____

DATE: _____ S M T W T F S

I AM GRATEFUL FOR:

1. _____
2. _____
3. _____

WHAT CAN I DO TO MAKE TODAY GREAT?

_____
_____
_____

WHAT WERE THE BEST MOMENTS FROM TODAY?

_____
_____

DATE: _____ S M T W T F S

I AM GRATEFUL FOR:

1. _____

2. _____

3. _____

WHAT CAN I DO TO MAKE TODAY GREAT?

_____

_____

_____

WHAT WERE THE BEST MOMENTS FROM TODAY?

_____

_____

_____

DATE: _____ S M T W T F S

I AM GRATEFUL FOR:

1. _____

2. _____

3. _____

WHAT CAN I DO TO MAKE TODAY GREAT?

_____

_____

_____

WHAT WERE THE BEST MOMENTS FROM TODAY?

_____

_____

reflection

What simple treats and comforts bring you joy?

DATE: _____ S M T W T F S

I AM GRATEFUL FOR:

1. _____

2. _____

3. _____

WHAT CAN I DO TO MAKE TODAY GREAT?

_____

_____

_____

WHAT WERE THE BEST MOMENTS FROM TODAY?

_____

_____

_____

DATE: _____ S M T W T F S

I AM GRATEFUL FOR:

1. _____

2. _____

3. _____

WHAT CAN I DO TO MAKE TODAY GREAT?

_____

_____

_____

WHAT WERE THE BEST MOMENTS FROM TODAY?

_____

_____

DATE: _____ S M T W T F S

I AM GRATEFUL FOR:

1. _____

2. _____

3. _____

WHAT CAN I DO TO MAKE TODAY GREAT?

_____

_____

_____

WHAT WERE THE BEST MOMENTS FROM TODAY?

_____

_____

_____

DATE: _____ S M T W T F S

I AM GRATEFUL FOR:

1. _____

2. _____

3. _____

WHAT CAN I DO TO MAKE TODAY GREAT?

_____

_____

_____

WHAT WERE THE BEST MOMENTS FROM TODAY?

_____

_____

_____

DATE: _____ S M T W T F S

I AM GRATEFUL FOR:

1. _____

2. _____

3. _____

WHAT CAN I DO TO MAKE TODAY GREAT?

_____

_____

_____

WHAT WERE THE BEST MOMENTS FROM TODAY?

_____

_____

_____

DATE: _____ S M T W T F S

I AM GRATEFUL FOR:

1. _____

2. _____

3. _____

WHAT CAN I DO TO MAKE TODAY GREAT?

_____

_____

_____

WHAT WERE THE BEST MOMENTS FROM TODAY?

_____

_____

_____

I will focus on what makes me happy.

DATE: _____ S M T W T F S

I AM GRATEFUL FOR:

1. _____

2. _____

3. _____

WHAT CAN I DO TO MAKE TODAY GREAT?

_____

_____

_____

WHAT WERE THE BEST MOMENTS FROM TODAY?

_____

_____

_____

DATE: _____ S M T W T F S

I AM GRATEFUL FOR:

1. _____

2. _____

3. _____

WHAT CAN I DO TO MAKE TODAY GREAT?

_____

_____

_____

WHAT WERE THE BEST MOMENTS FROM TODAY?

_____

_____

_____

DATE: _____ S M T W T F S

I AM GRATEFUL FOR:

1. _____

2. _____

3. _____

WHAT CAN I DO TO MAKE TODAY GREAT?

_____

_____

_____

WHAT WERE THE BEST MOMENTS FROM TODAY?

_____

_____

_____

DATE: _____ S M T W T F S

I AM GRATEFUL FOR:

1. _____

2. _____

3. _____

WHAT CAN I DO TO MAKE TODAY GREAT?

_____

_____

_____

WHAT WERE THE BEST MOMENTS FROM TODAY?

_____

_____

_____

DATE: _____ S M T W T F S

I AM GRATEFUL FOR:

1. _____

2. _____

3. _____

WHAT CAN I DO TO MAKE TODAY GREAT?

_____

_____

_____

WHAT WERE THE BEST MOMENTS FROM TODAY?

_____

_____

DATE: _____ S M T W T F S

I AM GRATEFUL FOR:

1. _____

2. _____

3. _____

WHAT CAN I DO TO MAKE TODAY GREAT?

_____

_____

WHAT WERE THE BEST MOMENTS FROM TODAY?

_____

_____

_____

A grateful heart is a magnet for miracles.

DATE: _____ S M T W T F S

I AM GRATEFUL FOR:

1. _____

2. _____

3. _____

WHAT CAN I DO TO MAKE TODAY GREAT?

_____

_____

_____

WHAT WERE THE BEST MOMENTS FROM TODAY?

_____

_____

_____

DATE: _____ S M T W T F S

I AM GRATEFUL FOR:

1. _____

2. _____

3. _____

WHAT CAN I DO TO MAKE TODAY GREAT?

_____

_____

_____

WHAT WERE THE BEST MOMENTS FROM TODAY?

_____

_____

_____

DATE: _____ S M T W T F S

I AM GRATEFUL FOR:

1. _____

2. _____

3. _____

WHAT CAN I DO TO MAKE TODAY GREAT?

_____

_____

_____

WHAT WERE THE BEST MOMENTS FROM TODAY?

_____

_____

_____

DATE: _____ S M T W T F S

I AM GRATEFUL FOR:

1. _____

2. _____

3. _____

WHAT CAN I DO TO MAKE TODAY GREAT?

_____

_____

_____

WHAT WERE THE BEST MOMENTS FROM TODAY?

_____

_____

_____

reflection

Describe the sensations
you feel when experiencing
gratitude.

DATE: _____ S M T W T F S

I AM GRATEFUL FOR:

1. _____

2. _____

3. _____

WHAT CAN I DO TO MAKE TODAY GREAT?

_____

_____

_____

WHAT WERE THE BEST MOMENTS FROM TODAY?

_____

_____

_____

DATE: _____ S M T W T F S

I AM GRATEFUL FOR:

1. _____

2. _____

3. _____

WHAT CAN I DO TO MAKE TODAY GREAT?

_____

_____

_____

WHAT WERE THE BEST MOMENTS FROM TODAY?

_____

_____

_____

DATE: _____ S M T W T F S

I AM GRATEFUL FOR:

1. _____

2. _____

3. _____

WHAT CAN I DO TO MAKE TODAY GREAT?

_____

_____

_____

WHAT WERE THE BEST MOMENTS FROM TODAY?

_____

_____

_____

DATE: _____ S M T W T F S

I AM GRATEFUL FOR:

1. _____

2. _____

3. _____

WHAT CAN I DO TO MAKE TODAY GREAT?

_____

_____

_____

WHAT WERE THE BEST MOMENTS FROM TODAY?

_____

_____

_____

DATE: _____ S M T W T F S

I AM GRATEFUL FOR:

1. _____

2. _____

3. _____

WHAT CAN I DO TO MAKE TODAY GREAT?

_____

_____

_____

WHAT WERE THE BEST MOMENTS FROM TODAY?

_____

_____

_____

DATE: _____ S M T W T F S

I AM GRATEFUL FOR:

1. _____

2. _____

3. _____

WHAT CAN I DO TO MAKE TODAY GREAT?

_____

_____

_____

WHAT WERE THE BEST MOMENTS FROM TODAY?

_____

_____

Happiness blooms from within.

DATE: _____ S M T W T F S

I AM GRATEFUL FOR:

1. _____

2. _____

3. _____

WHAT CAN I DO TO MAKE TODAY GREAT?

_____

_____

_____

WHAT WERE THE BEST MOMENTS FROM TODAY?

_____

_____

_____

DATE: _____ S M T W T F S

I AM GRATEFUL FOR:

1. _____

2. _____

3. _____

WHAT CAN I DO TO MAKE TODAY GREAT?

_____

_____

_____

WHAT WERE THE BEST MOMENTS FROM TODAY?

_____

_____

_____

DATE: _____ S M T W T F S

I AM GRATEFUL FOR:

1. _____

2. _____

3. _____

WHAT CAN I DO TO MAKE TODAY GREAT?

_____

_____

_____

WHAT WERE THE BEST MOMENTS FROM TODAY?

_____

_____

_____

DATE: _____ S M T W T F S

I AM GRATEFUL FOR:

1. _____

2. _____

3. _____

WHAT CAN I DO TO MAKE TODAY GREAT?

_____

_____

_____

WHAT WERE THE BEST MOMENTS FROM TODAY?

_____

_____

_____

DATE: _____ S M T W T F S

I AM GRATEFUL FOR:

1. _____

2. _____

3. _____

WHAT CAN I DO TO MAKE TODAY GREAT?

_____

_____

_____

WHAT WERE THE BEST MOMENTS FROM TODAY?

_____

_____

_____

DATE: _____ S M T W T F S

I AM GRATEFUL FOR:

1. _____

2. _____

3. _____

WHAT CAN I DO TO MAKE TODAY GREAT?

_____

_____

_____

WHAT WERE THE BEST MOMENTS FROM TODAY?

_____

_____

_____

I'm thankful for today.

DATE: _____ S M T W T F S

I AM GRATEFUL FOR:

1. _____

2. _____

3. _____

WHAT CAN I DO TO MAKE TODAY GREAT?

_____

_____

_____

WHAT WERE THE BEST MOMENTS FROM TODAY?

_____

_____

_____

DATE: _____ S M T W T F S

I AM GRATEFUL FOR:

1. _____

2. _____

3. _____

WHAT CAN I DO TO MAKE TODAY GREAT?

_____

_____

_____

WHAT WERE THE BEST MOMENTS FROM TODAY?

_____

_____

_____

DATE: _____ S M T W T F S

I AM GRATEFUL FOR:

1. _____

2. _____

3. _____

WHAT CAN I DO TO MAKE TODAY GREAT?

_____

_____

WHAT WERE THE BEST MOMENTS FROM TODAY?

_____

_____

DATE: _____ S M T W T F S

I AM GRATEFUL FOR:

1. _____

2. _____

3. _____

WHAT CAN I DO TO MAKE TODAY GREAT?

_____

_____

WHAT WERE THE BEST MOMENTS FROM TODAY?

_____

_____

reflection

Explain what you appreciate about the area you live in.

DATE: _____ S M T W T F S

I AM GRATEFUL FOR:

1. _____

2. _____

3. _____

WHAT CAN I DO TO MAKE TODAY GREAT?

_____

_____

_____

WHAT WERE THE BEST MOMENTS FROM TODAY?

_____

_____

_____

DATE: _____ S M T W T F S

I AM GRATEFUL FOR:

1. _____

2. _____

3. _____

WHAT CAN I DO TO MAKE TODAY GREAT?

_____

_____

_____

WHAT WERE THE BEST MOMENTS FROM TODAY?

_____

_____

_____

DATE: _____ S M T W T F S

I AM GRATEFUL FOR:

1. _____

2. _____

3. _____

WHAT CAN I DO TO MAKE TODAY GREAT?

_____

_____

_____

WHAT WERE THE BEST MOMENTS FROM TODAY?

_____

_____

_____

DATE: _____ S M T W T F S

I AM GRATEFUL FOR:

1. _____

2. _____

3. _____

WHAT CAN I DO TO MAKE TODAY GREAT?

_____

_____

_____

WHAT WERE THE BEST MOMENTS FROM TODAY?

_____

_____

DATE: _____ S M T W T F S

I AM GRATEFUL FOR:

1. _____

2. _____

3. _____

WHAT CAN I DO TO MAKE TODAY GREAT?

_____

_____

WHAT WERE THE BEST MOMENTS FROM TODAY?

_____

_____

DATE: _____ S M T W T F S

I AM GRATEFUL FOR:

1. _____

2. _____

3. _____

WHAT CAN I DO TO MAKE TODAY GREAT?

_____

_____

WHAT WERE THE BEST MOMENTS FROM TODAY?

_____

_____

It is not joy that makes us grateful. It is gratitude that makes us joyful.

DATE: _____ S M T W T F S

I AM GRATEFUL FOR:

1. _____
2. _____
3. _____

WHAT CAN I DO TO MAKE TODAY GREAT?

_____
_____
_____

WHAT WERE THE BEST MOMENTS FROM TODAY?

_____
_____
_____

DATE: _____ S M T W T F S

I AM GRATEFUL FOR:

1. _____

2. _____

3. _____

WHAT CAN I DO TO MAKE TODAY GREAT?

_____

_____

_____

WHAT WERE THE BEST MOMENTS FROM TODAY?

_____

_____

_____

DATE: _____ S M T W T F S

I AM GRATEFUL FOR:

1. _____

2. _____

3. _____

WHAT CAN I DO TO MAKE TODAY GREAT?

_____

_____

_____

WHAT WERE THE BEST MOMENTS FROM TODAY?

_____

_____

_____

DATE: _____ S M T W T F S

I AM GRATEFUL FOR:

1. _____

2. _____

3. _____

WHAT CAN I DO TO MAKE TODAY GREAT?

_____

_____

_____

WHAT WERE THE BEST MOMENTS FROM TODAY?

_____

_____

_____

DATE: _____ S M T W T F S

I AM GRATEFUL FOR:

1. _____

2. _____

3. _____

WHAT CAN I DO TO MAKE TODAY GREAT?

_____

_____

_____

WHAT WERE THE BEST MOMENTS FROM TODAY?

_____

_____

_____

DATE: _____ S M T W T F S

I AM GRATEFUL FOR:

1. _____

2. _____

3. _____

WHAT CAN I DO TO MAKE TODAY GREAT?

_____

_____

_____

WHAT WERE THE BEST MOMENTS FROM TODAY?

_____

_____

_____

Stay grateful.

DATE: _____ S M T W T F S

I AM GRATEFUL FOR:

1. _____
2. _____
3. _____

WHAT CAN I DO TO MAKE TODAY GREAT?

_____

_____

_____

WHAT WERE THE BEST MOMENTS FROM TODAY?

_____

_____

_____

DATE: _____ S M T W T F S

I AM GRATEFUL FOR:

1. _____
2. _____
3. _____

WHAT CAN I DO TO MAKE TODAY GREAT?

_____

_____

_____

WHAT WERE THE BEST MOMENTS FROM TODAY?

_____

_____

_____

DATE: _____ S M T W T F S

I AM GRATEFUL FOR:

1. _____

2. _____

3. _____

WHAT CAN I DO TO MAKE TODAY GREAT?

_____

_____

_____

WHAT WERE THE BEST MOMENTS FROM TODAY?

_____

_____

_____

DATE: _____ S M T W T F S

I AM GRATEFUL FOR:

1. _____

2. _____

3. _____

WHAT CAN I DO TO MAKE TODAY GREAT?

_____

_____

_____

WHAT WERE THE BEST MOMENTS FROM TODAY?

_____

_____

_____

reflection

How are your basic needs
being met today from
morning until night?

DATE: _____ S M T W T F S

I AM GRATEFUL FOR:

1. _____

2. _____

3. _____

WHAT CAN I DO TO MAKE TODAY GREAT?

_____

_____

_____

WHAT WERE THE BEST MOMENTS FROM TODAY?

_____

_____

_____

DATE: _____ S M T W T F S

I AM GRATEFUL FOR:

1. _____

2. _____

3. _____

WHAT CAN I DO TO MAKE TODAY GREAT?

_____

_____

_____

WHAT WERE THE BEST MOMENTS FROM TODAY?

_____

_____

_____

DATE: _____ S M T W T F S

I AM GRATEFUL FOR:

1. _____

2. _____

3. _____

WHAT CAN I DO TO MAKE TODAY GREAT?

_____

_____

_____

WHAT WERE THE BEST MOMENTS FROM TODAY?

_____

_____

_____

DATE: _____ S M T W T F S

I AM GRATEFUL FOR:

1. _____

2. _____

3. _____

WHAT CAN I DO TO MAKE TODAY GREAT?

_____

_____

_____

WHAT WERE THE BEST MOMENTS FROM TODAY?

_____

_____

DATE: _____ S M T W T F S

I AM GRATEFUL FOR:

1. _____

2. _____

3. _____

WHAT CAN I DO TO MAKE TODAY GREAT?

_____

_____

_____

WHAT WERE THE BEST MOMENTS FROM TODAY?

_____

_____

_____

DATE: _____ S M T W T F S

I AM GRATEFUL FOR:

1. _____

2. _____

3. _____

WHAT CAN I DO TO MAKE TODAY GREAT?

_____

_____

_____

WHAT WERE THE BEST MOMENTS FROM TODAY?

_____

_____

_____

Find joy in the ordinary.

DATE: _____ S M T W T F S

I AM GRATEFUL FOR:

1. _____

2. _____

3. _____

WHAT CAN I DO TO MAKE TODAY GREAT?

_____

_____

_____

WHAT WERE THE BEST MOMENTS FROM TODAY?

_____

_____

_____

DATE: _____ S M T W T F S

I AM GRATEFUL FOR:

1. _____

2. _____

3. _____

WHAT CAN I DO TO MAKE TODAY GREAT?

_____

_____

_____

WHAT WERE THE BEST MOMENTS FROM TODAY?

_____

_____

_____

DATE: _____ S M T W T F S

I AM GRATEFUL FOR:

1. _____

2. _____

3. _____

WHAT CAN I DO TO MAKE TODAY GREAT?

_____

_____

_____

WHAT WERE THE BEST MOMENTS FROM TODAY?

_____

_____

_____

DATE: _____ S M T W T F S

I AM GRATEFUL FOR:

1. _____

2. _____

3. _____

WHAT CAN I DO TO MAKE TODAY GREAT?

_____

_____

_____

WHAT WERE THE BEST MOMENTS FROM TODAY?

_____

_____

_____

DATE: _____ S M T W T F S

I AM GRATEFUL FOR:

1. _____

2. _____

3. _____

WHAT CAN I DO TO MAKE TODAY GREAT?

_____

_____

_____

WHAT WERE THE BEST MOMENTS FROM TODAY?

_____

_____

_____

DATE: _____ S M T W T F S

I AM GRATEFUL FOR:

1. _____

2. _____

3. _____

WHAT CAN I DO TO MAKE TODAY GREAT?

_____

_____

_____

WHAT WERE THE BEST MOMENTS FROM TODAY?

_____

_____

_____

Gratitude is a vitamin for the soul.

DATE: _____ S M T W T F S

I AM GRATEFUL FOR:

1. _____

2. _____

3. _____

WHAT CAN I DO TO MAKE TODAY GREAT?

_____

_____

_____

WHAT WERE THE BEST MOMENTS FROM TODAY?

_____

_____

_____

DATE: _____ S M T W T F S

I AM GRATEFUL FOR:

1. _____

2. _____

3. _____

WHAT CAN I DO TO MAKE TODAY GREAT?

_____

_____

_____

WHAT WERE THE BEST MOMENTS FROM TODAY?

_____

_____

_____

DATE: _____ S M T W T F S

I AM GRATEFUL FOR:

1. _____

2. _____

3. _____

WHAT CAN I DO TO MAKE TODAY GREAT?

_____

_____

_____

WHAT WERE THE BEST MOMENTS FROM TODAY?

_____

_____

_____

DATE: _____ S M T W T F S

I AM GRATEFUL FOR:

1. _____

2. _____

3. _____

WHAT CAN I DO TO MAKE TODAY GREAT?

_____

_____

_____

WHAT WERE THE BEST MOMENTS FROM TODAY?

_____

_____

reflection

DATE: _____ S M T W T F S

I AM GRATEFUL FOR:

1. _____

2. _____

3. _____

WHAT CAN I DO TO MAKE TODAY GREAT?

WHAT WERE THE BEST MOMENTS FROM TODAY?

DATE: _____ S M T W T F S

I AM GRATEFUL FOR:

1. _____

2. _____

3. _____

WHAT CAN I DO TO MAKE TODAY GREAT?

WHAT WERE THE BEST MOMENTS FROM TODAY?

DATE: _____ S M T W T F S

I AM GRATEFUL FOR:

1. _____

2. _____

3. _____

WHAT CAN I DO TO MAKE TODAY GREAT?

_____

_____

_____

WHAT WERE THE BEST MOMENTS FROM TODAY?

_____

_____

_____

DATE: _____ S M T W T F S

I AM GRATEFUL FOR:

1. _____

2. _____

3. _____

WHAT CAN I DO TO MAKE TODAY GREAT?

_____

_____

_____

WHAT WERE THE BEST MOMENTS FROM TODAY?

_____

_____

_____

DATE: _____ S M T W T F S

I AM GRATEFUL FOR:

1. _____

2. _____

3. _____

WHAT CAN I DO TO MAKE TODAY GREAT?

_____

_____

_____

WHAT WERE THE BEST MOMENTS FROM TODAY?

_____

_____

_____

DATE: _____ S M T W T F S

I AM GRATEFUL FOR:

1. _____

2. _____

3. _____

WHAT CAN I DO TO MAKE TODAY GREAT?

_____

_____

_____

WHAT WERE THE BEST MOMENTS FROM TODAY?

_____

_____

_____

Today is a great day to smile and be happy.

DATE: _____ S M T W T F S

I AM GRATEFUL FOR:

1. _____

2. _____

3. _____

WHAT CAN I DO TO MAKE TODAY GREAT?

_____

_____

WHAT WERE THE BEST MOMENTS FROM TODAY?

_____

_____

DATE: _____ S M T W T F S

I AM GRATEFUL FOR:

1. _____

2. _____

3. _____

WHAT CAN I DO TO MAKE TODAY GREAT?

_____

_____

_____

WHAT WERE THE BEST MOMENTS FROM TODAY?

_____

_____

_____

DATE: _____ S M T W T F S

I AM GRATEFUL FOR:

1. _____

2. _____

3. _____

WHAT CAN I DO TO MAKE TODAY GREAT?

_____

_____

_____

WHAT WERE THE BEST MOMENTS FROM TODAY?

_____

_____

_____

DATE: _____ S M T W T F S

I AM GRATEFUL FOR:

1. _____

2. _____

3. _____

WHAT CAN I DO TO MAKE TODAY GREAT?

_____

_____

_____

WHAT WERE THE BEST MOMENTS FROM TODAY?

_____

_____

_____

DATE: _____ S M T W T F S

I AM GRATEFUL FOR:

1. _____

2. _____

3. _____

WHAT CAN I DO TO MAKE TODAY GREAT?

_____

_____

_____

WHAT WERE THE BEST MOMENTS FROM TODAY?

_____

_____

_____

DATE: _____ S M T W T F S

I AM GRATEFUL FOR:

1. _____

2. _____

3. _____

WHAT CAN I DO TO MAKE TODAY GREAT?

_____

_____

_____

WHAT WERE THE BEST MOMENTS FROM TODAY?

_____

_____

_____

Exist to be happy, not to impress.

DATE: _____ S M T W T F S

I AM GRATEFUL FOR:

1. _____

2. _____

3. _____

WHAT CAN I DO TO MAKE TODAY GREAT?

_____

_____

_____

WHAT WERE THE BEST MOMENTS FROM TODAY?

_____

_____

_____

DATE: _____ S M T W T F S

I AM GRATEFUL FOR:

1. _____

2. _____

3. _____

WHAT CAN I DO TO MAKE TODAY GREAT?

_____

_____

_____

WHAT WERE THE BEST MOMENTS FROM TODAY?

_____

_____

DATE: _____ S M T W T F S

I AM GRATEFUL FOR:

1. _____

2. _____

3. _____

WHAT CAN I DO TO MAKE TODAY GREAT?

_____

_____

_____

WHAT WERE THE BEST MOMENTS FROM TODAY?

_____

_____

_____

DATE: _____ S M T W T F S

I AM GRATEFUL FOR:

1. _____

2. _____

3. _____

WHAT CAN I DO TO MAKE TODAY GREAT?

_____

_____

_____

WHAT WERE THE BEST MOMENTS FROM TODAY?

_____

_____

reflection

List the talents and admirable
qualities you've been
blessed with.

DATE: _____   S M T W T F S

I AM GRATEFUL FOR:

1. _____

2. _____

3. _____

WHAT CAN I DO TO MAKE TODAY GREAT?

_____

_____

_____

WHAT WERE THE BEST MOMENTS FROM TODAY?

_____

_____

_____

DATE: _____   S M T W T F S

I AM GRATEFUL FOR:

1. _____

2. _____

3. _____

WHAT CAN I DO TO MAKE TODAY GREAT?

_____

_____

_____

WHAT WERE THE BEST MOMENTS FROM TODAY?

_____

_____

_____

DATE: _____ S M T W T F S

I AM GRATEFUL FOR:

1. _____

2. _____

3. _____

WHAT CAN I DO TO MAKE TODAY GREAT?

_____

_____

_____

WHAT WERE THE BEST MOMENTS FROM TODAY?

_____

_____

_____

DATE: _____ S M T W T F S

I AM GRATEFUL FOR:

1. _____

2. _____

3. _____

WHAT CAN I DO TO MAKE TODAY GREAT?

_____

_____

_____

WHAT WERE THE BEST MOMENTS FROM TODAY?

_____

_____

DATE: _____ S M T W T F S

I AM GRATEFUL FOR:

1. _____

2. _____

3. _____

WHAT CAN I DO TO MAKE TODAY GREAT?

_____

_____

_____

WHAT WERE THE BEST MOMENTS FROM TODAY?

_____

_____

_____

DATE: _____ S M T W T F S

I AM GRATEFUL FOR:

1. _____

2. _____

3. _____

WHAT CAN I DO TO MAKE TODAY GREAT?

_____

_____

_____

WHAT WERE THE BEST MOMENTS FROM TODAY?

_____

_____

_____

*Be grateful for where
you are by appreciating
the road that got
you here.*

DATE: _____ S M T W T F S

I AM GRATEFUL FOR:

1. _____

2. _____

3. _____

WHAT CAN I DO TO MAKE TODAY GREAT?

_____

_____

WHAT WERE THE BEST MOMENTS FROM TODAY?

_____

_____

_____

DATE: _____ S M T W T F S

I AM GRATEFUL FOR:

1. _____

2. _____

3. _____

WHAT CAN I DO TO MAKE TODAY GREAT?

_____

_____

_____

WHAT WERE THE BEST MOMENTS FROM TODAY?

_____

_____

_____

DATE: _____ S M T W T F S

I AM GRATEFUL FOR:

1. _____

2. _____

3. _____

WHAT CAN I DO TO MAKE TODAY GREAT?

_____

_____

_____

WHAT WERE THE BEST MOMENTS FROM TODAY?

_____

_____

_____

DATE: _____ S M T W T F S

I AM GRATEFUL FOR:

1. _____

2. _____

3. _____

WHAT CAN I DO TO MAKE TODAY GREAT?

_____

_____

_____

WHAT WERE THE BEST MOMENTS FROM TODAY?

_____

_____

_____

DATE: _____ S M T W T F S

I AM GRATEFUL FOR:

1. _____

2. _____

3. _____

WHAT CAN I DO TO MAKE TODAY GREAT?

_____

_____

_____

WHAT WERE THE BEST MOMENTS FROM TODAY?

_____

_____

_____

DATE: _____ S M T W T F S

I AM GRATEFUL FOR:

1. _____

2. _____

3. _____

WHAT CAN I DO TO MAKE TODAY GREAT?

_____

_____

_____

WHAT WERE THE BEST MOMENTS FROM TODAY?

_____

_____

_____

Today is a gift.

DATE: _____ S M T W T F S

I AM GRATEFUL FOR:

1. _____

2. _____

3. _____

WHAT CAN I DO TO MAKE TODAY GREAT?

_____

_____

_____

WHAT WERE THE BEST MOMENTS FROM TODAY?

_____

_____

_____

DATE: _____ S M T W T F S

I AM GRATEFUL FOR:

1. _____

2. _____

3. _____

WHAT CAN I DO TO MAKE TODAY GREAT?

_____

_____

_____

WHAT WERE THE BEST MOMENTS FROM TODAY?

_____

_____

_____

DATE: _____ S M T W T F S

I AM GRATEFUL FOR:

1. _____

2. _____

3. _____

WHAT CAN I DO TO MAKE TODAY GREAT?

_____

_____

_____

WHAT WERE THE BEST MOMENTS FROM TODAY?

_____

_____

_____

DATE: _____ S M T W T F S

I AM GRATEFUL FOR:

1. _____

2. _____

3. _____

WHAT CAN I DO TO MAKE TODAY GREAT?

_____

_____

_____

WHAT WERE THE BEST MOMENTS FROM TODAY?

_____

_____

_____

reflection

Describe a time when you
received a sentimental gift
and what it meant to you.

DATE: _____ S M T W T F S

I AM GRATEFUL FOR:

1. _____

2. _____

3. _____

WHAT CAN I DO TO MAKE TODAY GREAT?

_____

_____

_____

WHAT WERE THE BEST MOMENTS FROM TODAY?

_____

_____

_____

DATE: _____ S M T W T F S

I AM GRATEFUL FOR:

1. _____

2. _____

3. _____

WHAT CAN I DO TO MAKE TODAY GREAT?

_____

_____

_____

WHAT WERE THE BEST MOMENTS FROM TODAY?

_____

_____

_____

DATE: _____ S M T W T F S

I AM GRATEFUL FOR:

1. _____

2. _____

3. _____

WHAT CAN I DO TO MAKE TODAY GREAT?

_____

_____

_____

WHAT WERE THE BEST MOMENTS FROM TODAY?

_____

_____

_____

DATE: _____ S M T W T F S

I AM GRATEFUL FOR:

1. _____

2. _____

3. _____

WHAT CAN I DO TO MAKE TODAY GREAT?

_____

_____

_____

WHAT WERE THE BEST MOMENTS FROM TODAY?

_____

_____

_____

DATE: _____ S M T W T F S

I AM GRATEFUL FOR:

1. _____

2. _____

3. _____

WHAT CAN I DO TO MAKE TODAY GREAT?

_____

_____

_____

WHAT WERE THE BEST MOMENTS FROM TODAY?

_____

_____

_____

DATE: _____ S M T W T F S

I AM GRATEFUL FOR:

1. _____

2. _____

3. _____

WHAT CAN I DO TO MAKE TODAY GREAT?

_____

_____

_____

WHAT WERE THE BEST MOMENTS FROM TODAY?

_____

_____

*Some people complain
that flowers have thorns.
I am grateful that
thorns have flowers.*

DATE: _____ S M T W T F S

I AM GRATEFUL FOR:

1. _____

2. _____

3. _____

WHAT CAN I DO TO MAKE TODAY GREAT?

_____

_____

_____

WHAT WERE THE BEST MOMENTS FROM TODAY?

_____

_____

DATE: _____ S M T W T F S

I AM GRATEFUL FOR:

1. _____

2. _____

3. _____

WHAT CAN I DO TO MAKE TODAY GREAT?

_____

_____

_____

WHAT WERE THE BEST MOMENTS FROM TODAY?

_____

_____

_____

DATE: _____ S M T W T F S

I AM GRATEFUL FOR:

1. _____

2. _____

3. _____

WHAT CAN I DO TO MAKE TODAY GREAT?

_____

_____

_____

WHAT WERE THE BEST MOMENTS FROM TODAY?

_____

_____

_____

DATE: _____ S M T W T F S

I AM GRATEFUL FOR:

1. _____

2. _____

3. _____

WHAT CAN I DO TO MAKE TODAY GREAT?

_____

_____

_____

WHAT WERE THE BEST MOMENTS FROM TODAY?

_____

_____

_____

DATE: _____ S M T W T F S

I AM GRATEFUL FOR:

1. _____

2. _____

3. _____

WHAT CAN I DO TO MAKE TODAY GREAT?

_____

_____

_____

WHAT WERE THE BEST MOMENTS FROM TODAY?

_____

_____

_____

DATE: _____ S M T W T F S

I AM GRATEFUL FOR:

1. _____

2. _____

3. _____

WHAT CAN I DO TO MAKE TODAY GREAT?

_____

_____

_____

WHAT WERE THE BEST MOMENTS FROM TODAY?

_____

_____

_____

The more you look for the good, the more you will be able to find it.

DATE: _____ S M T W T F S

I AM GRATEFUL FOR:

1. _____

2. _____

3. _____

WHAT CAN I DO TO MAKE TODAY GREAT?

_____

_____

_____

WHAT WERE THE BEST MOMENTS FROM TODAY?

_____

_____

_____

DATE: _____ S M T W T F S

I AM GRATEFUL FOR:

1. _____

2. _____

3. _____

WHAT CAN I DO TO MAKE TODAY GREAT?

_____

_____

_____

WHAT WERE THE BEST MOMENTS FROM TODAY?

_____

_____

_____

DATE: _____ S M T W T F S

I AM GRATEFUL FOR:

1. _____

2. _____

3. _____

WHAT CAN I DO TO MAKE TODAY GREAT?

_____

_____

_____

WHAT WERE THE BEST MOMENTS FROM TODAY?

_____

_____

_____

DATE: _____ S M T W T F S

I AM GRATEFUL FOR:

1. _____

2. _____

3. _____

WHAT CAN I DO TO MAKE TODAY GREAT?

_____

_____

_____

WHAT WERE THE BEST MOMENTS FROM TODAY?

_____

_____

reflection

List all the things you are
looking forward to, large
and small.